CW00405402

GROW
with goals

A step-by-step guide to setting and achieving positively-impacting goals

Workbook
(A companion to the guide book)

'Doyin Olorunfemi

GROW with Goals

A step-by-step guide to setting and achieving positively-impacting goals

Workbook

(A companion to the guide book)

'Doyin Olorunfemi

ISBN: 1718851677

ISBN-13: 978-1718851672

Cover design and layout by he**art'n'design**
(*a service of the* **EarthWake Media Group Ltd**)

Dedication

This book is dedicated to my family. My desire to be my best self for you inspired me to acquire the skills I now share with people around the world. You are my best "school" and the most impactful "degree" I have ever earned. I look forward to many more years of learning and growing through you.

And to You, God, who gives me these acronyms that always touch my life in unusual ways; thank you for entrusting me with ideas that change my world.

#LiveWell, #LiveFull and #LiveOut

Contents

Workbook

Chapter

Wheel of Life

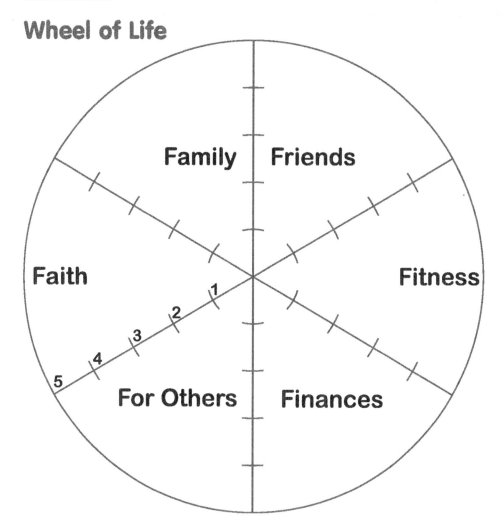

My SMART Goals

1. Clarify & Define

2. Create Visual Representation

3. Track for the year

4. Own your goals in 30 days

After you've read the relevant sections in Chapter 1, look through my example and use it as a prototype for writing your goals. The recommended maximum is 10.

Clarify & Define

What I would like to achieve

I would like to be fit and able to wear my size 14 clothes with ease. I would also like to run up the stairs without panting and have a flatter tummy

Why I want this goal

My weight is affecting my health and my protruding tummy is affecting my self confidence.

When I want this goal by

Christmas this year. I want to start next year healthy and confident

The effect of this goal on my overall life vision is

Longevity of life so I can live long enough to achieve all I believe I am here to achieve

How will I reward myself once achieved

I will treat myself to a new dress, budget £100

Steps to achieve this goal

1. Walk 30 mins daily
2. Planks and stomach exercise daily
3. Reduce my carb intake and seek advice on my diet options
4. Join an accountability group
5. Cycle for 1 hour every week
6.

My SMART goal statement

I will weigh 75kg and be a true size 14, with waist line of 28 inches by 1st December 2018

My Goal in Pictures

Tracking my goal

Goal *I would like to be fit and able to wear my size 14 clothes with ease. I would also like to run up the stairs without panting and have a flatter tummy*

Month 1   *January 2018*

On track ☐   Not on track ☑   Demotivated ☐   Stopped ☐

Notes *Cycling has been a bit of a challenge and I might have to consider joining a group. The walking is however going fine. I don't enjoy the crunches and planks.*

Month 2   *February 2018*

On track ☐   Not on track ☐   Demotivated ☑   Stopped ☐

Notes *Since falling off the bike, I haven't had the confidence to restart. Diet is going very well, I discovered the joys of green smoothie☺. Walking still going good.*

Month 3   *March 2018*

On track ☑   Not on track ☐   Demotivated ☐   Stopped ☐

Notes *I am so excited right now, I can hardly contain myself. End of month figures shows I have lost 25% of weight required and lost 2 inches on my waist. Smoothies forever!*

Month 4

On track ☐   Not on track ☐   Demotivated ☐   Stopped ☐

Notes

Month 5

On track ☐   Not on track ☐   Demotivated ☐   Stopped ☐

Notes

Month 6

On track ☐   Not on track ☐   Demotivated ☐   Stopped ☐

Notes

Tracking my goal (continued)

Month 7

On track ☐   Not on track ☐   Demotivated ☐   Stopped ☐

Notes

Month 8

On track ☐   Not on track ☐   Demotivated ☐   Stopped ☐

Notes

Month 9

On track ☐   Not on track ☐   Demotivated ☐   Stopped ☐

Notes

Month 10

On track ☐   Not on track ☐   Demotivated ☐   Stopped ☐

Notes

Month 11

On track ☐   Not on track ☐   Demotivated ☐   Stopped ☐

Notes

Month 12

On track ☐   Not on track ☐   Demotivated ☐   Stopped ☐

Notes

I achieved my goal: Yes ☐   No ☐

Comments

GOAL No. 1

What I would like to achieve

Why I want this goal

When I want this goal by

The effect of this goal on my overall life vision is

How will I reward myself once achieved

Steps to achieve this goal

1.
2.
3.
4.
5.
6.

My SMART goal statement

My Goal in Pictures

Tracking my goal

Goal

Month 1
On track ☐   **Not on track** ☐   **Demotivated** ☐   **Stopped** ☐
Notes

Month 2
On track ☐   **Not on track** ☐   **Demotivated** ☐   **Stopped** ☐
Notes

Month 3
On track ☐   **Not on track** ☐   **Demotivated** ☐   **Stopped** ☐
Notes

Month 4
On track ☐   **Not on track** ☐   **Demotivated** ☐   **Stopped** ☐
Notes

Month 5
On track ☐   **Not on track** ☐   **Demotivated** ☐   **Stopped** ☐
Notes

Month 6
On track ☐   **Not on track** ☐   **Demotivated** ☐   **Stopped** ☐
Notes

Tracking my goal (continued)

Month 7
On track ☐ Not on track ☐ Demotivated ☐ Stopped ☐
Notes

Month 8
On track ☐ Not on track ☐ Demotivated ☐ Stopped ☐
Notes

Month 9
On track ☐ Not on track ☐ Demotivated ☐ Stopped ☐
Notes

Month 10
On track ☐ Not on track ☐ Demotivated ☐ Stopped ☐
Notes

Month 11
On track ☐ Not on track ☐ Demotivated ☐ Stopped ☐
Notes

Month 12
On track ☐ Not on track ☐ Demotivated ☐ Stopped ☐
Notes

I achieved my goal: Yes ☐   No ☐
Comments

GOAL No. 2

What I would like to achieve

Why I want this goal

When I want this goal by

The effect of this goal on my overall life vision is

How will I reward myself once achieved

Steps to achieve this goal

1.
2.
3.
4.
5.
6.

My SMART goal statement

My Goal in Pictures

Tracking my goal

Goal

Month 1

On track ☐   Not on track ☐   Demotivated ☐   Stopped ☐

Notes

Month 2

On track ☐   Not on track ☐   Demotivated ☐   Stopped ☐

Notes

Month 3

On track ☐   Not on track ☐   Demotivated ☐   Stopped ☐

Notes

Month 4

On track ☐   Not on track ☐   Demotivated ☐   Stopped ☐

Notes

Month 5

On track ☐   Not on track ☐   Demotivated ☐   Stopped ☐

Notes

Month 6

On track ☐   Not on track ☐   Demotivated ☐   Stopped ☐

Notes

Tracking my goal (continued)

Month 7

On track ☐   Not on track ☐   Demotivated ☐   Stopped ☐

Notes

Month 8

On track ☐   Not on track ☐   Demotivated ☐   Stopped ☐

Notes

Month 9

On track ☐   Not on track ☐   Demotivated ☐   Stopped ☐

Notes

Month 10

On track ☐   Not on track ☐   Demotivated ☐   Stopped ☐

Notes

Month 11

On track ☐   Not on track ☐   Demotivated ☐   Stopped ☐

Notes

Month 12

On track ☐   Not on track ☐   Demotivated ☐   Stopped ☐

Notes

I achieved my goal: Yes ☐   No ☐

Comments

GOAL No. 3

What I would like to achieve

Why I want this goal

When I want this goal by

The effect of this goal on my overall life vision is

How will I reward myself once achieved

Steps to achieve this goal

1.
2.
3.
4.
5.
6.

My SMART goal statement

My Goal in Pictures

Tracking my goal

Goal

Month 1

On track ☐ Not on track ☐ Demotivated ☐ Stopped ☐

Notes

Month 2

On track ☐ Not on track ☐ Demotivated ☐ Stopped ☐

Notes

Month 3

On track ☐ Not on track ☐ Demotivated ☐ Stopped ☐

Notes

Month 4

On track ☐ Not on track ☐ Demotivated ☐ Stopped ☐

Notes

Month 5

On track ☐ Not on track ☐ Demotivated ☐ Stopped ☐

Notes

Month 6

On track ☐ Not on track ☐ Demotivated ☐ Stopped ☐

Notes

Tracking my goal (continued)

Month 7
On track ■   Not on track ■   Demotivated ■   Stopped ■
Notes
....
....
....

Month 8
On track ■   Not on track ■   Demotivated ■   Stopped ■
Notes
....
....
....

Month 9
On track ■   Not on track ■   Demotivated ■   Stopped ■
Notes
....
....
....

Month 10
On track ■   Not on track ■   Demotivated ■   Stopped ■
Notes
....
....
....

Month 11
On track ■   Not on track ■   Demotivated ■   Stopped ■
Notes
....
....
....

Month 12
On track ■   Not on track ■   Demotivated ■   Stopped ■
Notes
....
....
....

I achieved my goal: Yes ■   No ■
Comments
....
....
....

GOAL No. 4

What I would like to achieve

Why I want this goal

When I want this goal by

The effect of this goal on my overall life vision is

How will I reward myself once achieved

Steps to achieve this goal

1.
2.
3.
4.
5.
6.

My SMART goal statement

My Goal in Pictures

Tracking my goal

Goal
....
....
....

Month 1
On track ☐   Not on track ☐   Demotivated ☐   Stopped ☐
Notes
....
....

Month 2
On track ☐   Not on track ☐   Demotivated ☐   Stopped ☐
Notes
....
....

Month 3
On track ☐   Not on track ☐   Demotivated ☐   Stopped ☐
Notes
....
....

Month 4
On track ☐   Not on track ☐   Demotivated ☐   Stopped ☐
Notes
....
....

Month 5
On track ☐   Not on track ☐   Demotivated ☐   Stopped ☐
Notes
....
....

Month 6
On track ☐   Not on track ☐   Demotivated ☐   Stopped ☐
Notes
....
....

Tracking my goal (continued)

Month 7
On track ☐   Not on track ☐   Demotivated ☐   Stopped ☐
Notes

....

....

Month 8
On track ☐   Not on track ☐   Demotivated ☐   Stopped ☐
Notes

....

....

Month 9
On track ☐   Not on track ☐   Demotivated ☐   Stopped ☐
Notes

....

....

Month 10
On track ☐   Not on track ☐   Demotivated ☐   Stopped ☐
Notes

....

....

Month 11
On track ☐   Not on track ☐   Demotivated ☐   Stopped ☐
Notes

....

....

Month 12
On track ☐   Not on track ☐   Demotivated ☐   Stopped ☐
Notes

....

....

I achieved my goal: Yes ☐   No ☐
Comments

....

....

GOAL No. 5

What I would like to achieve

Why I want this goal

When I want this goal by

The effect of this goal on my overall life vision is

How will I reward myself once achieved

Steps to achieve this goal

1.
2.
3.
4.
5.
6.

My SMART goal statement

My Goal in Pictures

Tracking my goal

Goal

Month 1

On track ▢   Not on track ▢   Demotivated ▢   Stopped ▢

Notes

Month 2

On track ▢   Not on track ▢   Demotivated ▢   Stopped ▢

Notes

Month 3

On track ▢   Not on track ▢   Demotivated ▢   Stopped ▢

Notes

Month 4

On track ▢   Not on track ▢   Demotivated ▢   Stopped ▢

Notes

Month 5

On track ▢   Not on track ▢   Demotivated ▢   Stopped ▢

Notes

Month 6

On track ▢   Not on track ▢   Demotivated ▢   Stopped ▢

Notes

Tracking my goal (continued)

Month 7
On track ☐   Not on track ☐   Demotivated ☐   Stopped ☐
Notes
- -

- -

Month 8
On track ☐   Not on track ☐   Demotivated ☐   Stopped ☐
Notes
- -

- -

Month 9
On track ☐   Not on track ☐   Demotivated ☐   Stopped ☐
Notes
- -

- -

Month 10
On track ☐   Not on track ☐   Demotivated ☐   Stopped ☐
Notes
- -

- -

Month 11
On track ☐   Not on track ☐   Demotivated ☐   Stopped ☐
Notes
- -

- -

Month 12
On track ☐   Not on track ☐   Demotivated ☐   Stopped ☐
Notes
- -

- -

I achieved my goal: Yes ☐   No ☐
Comments
- -

- -

GOAL No. 6

What I would like to achieve

....
....
....

Why I want this goal

....
....
....

When I want this goal by

....

The effect of this goal on my overall life vision is

....
....
....

How will I reward myself once achieved

....
....
....

Steps to achieve this goal

1. ....
2. ....
3. ....
4. ....
5. ....
6. ....

My SMART goal statement

....
....
....
....

My Goal in Pictures

Tracking my goal

Goal

Month 1
On track ☐   Not on track ☐   Demotivated ☐   Stopped ☐
Notes

Month 2
On track ☐   Not on track ☐   Demotivated ☐   Stopped ☐
Notes

Month 3
On track ☐   Not on track ☐   Demotivated ☐   Stopped ☐
Notes

Month 4
On track ☐   Not on track ☐   Demotivated ☐   Stopped ☐
Notes

Month 5
On track ☐   Not on track ☐   Demotivated ☐   Stopped ☐
Notes

Month 6
On track ☐   Not on track ☐   Demotivated ☐   Stopped ☐
Notes

Tracking my goal (continued)

Month 7
On track ☐ Not on track ☐ Demotivated ☐ Stopped ☐
Notes ....

....

Month 8
On track ☐ Not on track ☐ Demotivated ☐ Stopped ☐
Notes ....

....

Month 9
On track ☐ Not on track ☐ Demotivated ☐ Stopped ☐
Notes ....

....

Month 10
On track ☐ Not on track ☐ Demotivated ☐ Stopped ☐
Notes ....

....

Month 11
On track ☐ Not on track ☐ Demotivated ☐ Stopped ☐
Notes ....

....

Month 12
On track ☐ Not on track ☐ Demotivated ☐ Stopped ☐
Notes ....

....

I achieved my goal: Yes ☐   No ☐
Comments ....

....

....

GOAL No. 7

What I would like to achieve

Why I want this goal

When I want this goal by

The effect of this goal on my overall life vision is

How will I reward myself once achieved

Steps to achieve this goal

1.
2.
3.
4.
5.
6.

My SMART goal statement

My Goal in Pictures

Tracking my goal

Goal

....

....

....

Month 1

On track ☐ Not on track ☐ Demotivated ☐ Stopped ☐

Notes

....

....

Month 2

On track ☐ Not on track ☐ Demotivated ☐ Stopped ☐

Notes

....

....

Month 3

On track ☐ Not on track ☐ Demotivated ☐ Stopped ☐

Notes

....

....

Month 4

On track ☐ Not on track ☐ Demotivated ☐ Stopped ☐

Notes

....

....

Month 5

On track ☐ Not on track ☐ Demotivated ☐ Stopped ☐

Notes

....

....

Month 6

On track ☐ Not on track ☐ Demotivated ☐ Stopped ☐

Notes

....

....

Tracking my goal (continued)

Month 7
On track ☐　　Not on track ☐　　Demotivated ☐　　Stopped ☐
Notes

....

....

Month 8
On track ☐　　Not on track ☐　　Demotivated ☐　　Stopped ☐
Notes

....

....

Month 9
On track ☐　　Not on track ☐　　Demotivated ☐　　Stopped ☐
Notes

....

....

Month 10
On track ☐　　Not on track ☐　　Demotivated ☐　　Stopped ☐
Notes

....

....

Month 11
On track ☐　　Not on track ☐　　Demotivated ☐　　Stopped ☐
Notes

....

....

Month 12
On track ☐　　Not on track ☐　　Demotivated ☐　　Stopped ☐
Notes

....

....

I achieved my goal:　　Yes ☐　　　No ☐
Comments

....

....

GOAL No. 8

What I would like to achieve

Why I want this goal

When I want this goal by

The effect of this goal on my overall life vision is

How will I reward myself once achieved

Steps to achieve this goal

1.
2.
3.
4.
5.
6.

My SMART goal statement

My Goal in Pictures

Tracking my goal

Goal

....
....
....

Month 1
On track ☐   Not on track ☐   Demotivated ☐   Stopped ☐
Notes

....
....

Month 2
On track ☐   Not on track ☐   Demotivated ☐   Stopped ☐
Notes

....
....

Month 3
On track ☐   Not on track ☐   Demotivated ☐   Stopped ☐
Notes

....
....

Month 4
On track ☐   Not on track ☐   Demotivated ☐   Stopped ☐
Notes

....
....

Month 5
On track ☐   Not on track ☐   Demotivated ☐   Stopped ☐
Notes

....
....

Month 6
On track ☐   Not on track ☐   Demotivated ☐   Stopped ☐
Notes

....
....

Tracking my goal (continued)

Month 7
On track ☐   Not on track ☐   Demotivated ☐   Stopped ☐
Notes ....

....

....

Month 8
On track ☐   Not on track ☐   Demotivated ☐   Stopped ☐
Notes ....

....

....

Month 9
On track ☐   Not on track ☐   Demotivated ☐   Stopped ☐
Notes ....

....

....

Month 10
On track ☐   Not on track ☐   Demotivated ☐   Stopped ☐
Notes ....

....

....

Month 11
On track ☐   Not on track ☐   Demotivated ☐   Stopped ☐
Notes ....

....

....

Month 12
On track ☐   Not on track ☐   Demotivated ☐   Stopped ☐
Notes ....

....

....

I achieved my goal: Yes ☐   No ☐
Comments ....

....

....

GOAL No. 9

What I would like to achieve

Why I want this goal

When I want this goal by

The effect of this goal on my overall life vision is

How will I reward myself once achieved

Steps to achieve this goal

1.
2.
3.
4.
5.
6.

My SMART goal statement

My Goal in Pictures

Tracking my goal

Goal

Month 1
On track ■   Not on track ■   Demotivated ■   Stopped ■
Notes

Month 2
On track ■   Not on track ■   Demotivated ■   Stopped ■
Notes

Month 3
On track ■   Not on track ■   Demotivated ■   Stopped ■
Notes

Month 4
On track ■   Not on track ■   Demotivated ■   Stopped ■
Notes

Month 5
On track ■   Not on track ■   Demotivated ■   Stopped ■
Notes

Month 6
On track ■   Not on track ■   Demotivated ■   Stopped ■
Notes

Tracking my goal (continued)

Month 7
On track ☐   Not on track ☐   Demotivated ☐   Stopped ☐
Notes

Month 8
On track ☐   Not on track ☐   Demotivated ☐   Stopped ☐
Notes

Month 9
On track ☐   Not on track ☐   Demotivated ☐   Stopped ☐
Notes

Month 10
On track ☐   Not on track ☐   Demotivated ☐   Stopped ☐
Notes

Month 11
On track ☐   Not on track ☐   Demotivated ☐   Stopped ☐
Notes

Month 12
On track ☐   Not on track ☐   Demotivated ☐   Stopped ☐
Notes

I achieved my goal: Yes ☐   No ☐
Comments

GOAL No. 10

What I would like to achieve

....
....
....

Why I want this goal

....
....
....

When I want this goal by

....

The effect of this goal on my overall life vision is

....
....
....

How will I reward myself once achieved

....
....
....

Steps to achieve this goal

1. ....
2. ....
3. ....
4. ....
5. ....
6. ....

My SMART goal statement

....
....
....
....

My Goal in Pictures

Tracking my goal

Goal
....
....
....

Month 1
On track ■ Not on track■ Demotivated■   Stopped■
Notes
....
....

Month 2
On track ■ Not on track■ Demotivated■   Stopped■
Notes
....
....

Month 3
On track ■ Not on track■ Demotivated■   Stopped■
Notes
....
....

Month 4
On track ■ Not on track■ Demotivated■   Stopped■
Notes
....
....

Month 5
On track ■ Not on track■ Demotivated■   Stopped■
Notes
....
....

Month 6
On track ■ Not on track■ Demotivated■   Stopped■
Notes
....
....

Tracking my goal (continued)

Month 7
On track ☐   Not on track ☐   Demotivated ☐   Stopped ☐
Notes
....

....

Month 8
On track ☐   Not on track ☐   Demotivated ☐   Stopped ☐
Notes
....

....

Month 9
On track ☐   Not on track ☐   Demotivated ☐   Stopped ☐
Notes
....

....

Month 10
On track ☐   Not on track ☐   Demotivated ☐   Stopped ☐
Notes
....

....

Month 11
On track ☐   Not on track ☐   Demotivated ☐   Stopped ☐
Notes
....

....

Month 12
On track ☐   Not on track ☐   Demotivated ☐   Stopped ☐
Notes
....

....

I achieved my goal: Yes ☐   No ☐
Comments
....

....

Day 1

1

2

3

4

5

6

7

8

9

10

Day 2

1

2

3

4

5

6

7

8

9

10

Day 3

1

2

3

4

5

6

7

8

9

10

Day 4

1
....
....
....

2
....
....
....

3
....
....
....

4
....
....
....

5
....
....
....

6
....
....
....

7
....
....
....

8
....
....
....

9
....
....
....

10
....
....
....

Day 5

1

2

3

4

5

6

7

8

9

10

Day 6

1
_____
_____
_____

2
_____
_____
_____

3
_____
_____
_____

4
_____
_____
_____

5
_____
_____
_____

6
_____
_____
_____

7
_____
_____
_____

8
_____
_____
_____

9
_____
_____
_____

10
_____
_____
_____

Day 7

1

2

3

4

5

6

7

8

9

10

Day 8

1

2

3

4

5

6

7

8

9

10

Day 9

1

2

3

4

5

6

7

8

9

10

Day 10

1 ....
....
....

2 ....
....
....

3 ....
....
....

4 ....
....
....

5 ....
....
....

6 ....
....
....

7 ....
....
....

8 ....
....
....

9 ....
....
....

10 ....
....
....

Day 11

1

2

3

4

5

6

7

8

9

10

Day 12

1

2

3

4

5

6

7

8

9

10

Day 13

1

2

3

4

5

6

7

8

9

10

Day 14

1 ....
....
....

2 ....
....
....

3 ....
....
....

4 ....
....
....

5 ....
....
....

6 ....
....
....

7 ....
....
....

8 ....
....
....

9 ....
....
....

10 ....
....
....

Day 15

1 ....

....

....

2 ....

....

....

3 ....

....

....

4 ....

....

....

5 ....

....

....

6 ....

....

....

7 ....

....

....

8 ....

....

....

9 ....

....

....

10 ....

....

....

Day 16

1
....
....
....

2
....
....
....

3
....
....
....

4
....
....
....

5
....
....
....

6
....
....
....

7
....
....
....

8
....
....
....

9
....
....
....

10
....
....
....

Day 17

1

2

3

4

5

6

7

8

9

10

Day 18

1

2

3

4

5

6

7

8

9

10

Day 19

1

2

3

4

5

6

7

8

9

10

Day 20

1

2

3

4

5

6

7

8

9

10

Day 21

1
....
....
....

2
....
....
....

3
....
....
....

4
....
....
....

5
....
....
....

6
....
....
....

7
....
....
....

8
....
....
....

9
....
....
....

10
....
....
....

Day 22

1
....
....
....

2
....
....
....

3
....
....
....

4
....
....
....

5
....
....
....

6
....
....
....

7
....
....
....

8
....
....
....

9
....
....
....

10
....
....
....

Day 23

1

2

3

4

5

6

7

8

9

10

Day 24

1
....
....
....

2
....
....
....

3
....
....
....

4
....
....
....

5
....
....
....

6
....
....
....

7
....
....
....

8
....
....
....

9
....
....
....

10
....
....
....

Day 25

1

2

3

4

5

6

7

8

9

10

Day 26

1

2

3

4

5

6

7

8

9

10

Day 27

1 ....

....

....

2 ....

....

....

3 ....

....

....

4 ....

....

....

5 ....

....

....

6 ....

....

....

7 ....

....

....

8 ....

....

....

9 ....

....

....

10 ....

....

....

Day 28

1
....
....
....

2
....
....
....

3
....
....
....

4
....
....
....

5
....
....
....

6
....
....
....

7
....
....
....

8
....
....
....

9
....
....
....

10
....
....
....

Day 29

1

2

3

4

5

6

7

8

9

10

Day 30

1
....
....
....

2
....
....
....

3
....
....
....

4
....
....
....

5
....
....
....

6
....
....
....

7
....
....
....

8
....
....
....

9
....
....
....

10
....
....
....

Chapter 2

Resourcing You

1. Create a list from your GAP

- Gains

- Avoid

- Partner

2. Rank the items on this list and specify the order in which they should be carried out

3. Put a comment that helps you kick-start this task

4. If unsure, use my example as a prototype.

Note: You have a page for 2 goals and they don't have to be completed at the beginning. You can add more items later. My suggestion will be to fill this section out with a pencil so you can easily edit your list.

GAP Chart (Example)

Goal	GAP List	Ranking (Order to do them)	Comments
I will write and publish a book on Goals by 31st May 2018	Research on the contrary views to goal setting (GAIN)	2	Make Google your friend!
	Interview and get stories of people who have excelled in each area (PARTNER)	4	Who set clear goals? Who has had to resource herself the most? Who is extremely organised? Who works consistently?
	Create time to write by cutting 2 hours off sleep for 30 days (AVOID)	1	Wake up at 2am instead of the normal 4am on Monday to Friday
	Document goals and how I achieved them in the last 3 months	3	Make use of your journal and write lightbulb moments, etc
	Editing course? (GAIN)	5	Delegate this, there's just no time to gain expertise in this area

GAP Chart

Goal	GAP List	Ranking (Order to do them)	Comments

GAP Chart

Goal	GAP List	Ranking (Order to do them)	Comments

GAP Chart

Goal	GAP List	Ranking (Order to do them)	Comments

GAP Chart

Goal	GAP List	Ranking (Order to do them)	Comments

As step-by-step guide to achieving positively impacting goals

GAP Chart

Goal	GAP List	Ranking (Order to do them)	Comments

WB85

GAP Chart

Goal	GAP List	Ranking (Order to do them)	Comments

GAP Chart

Goal	GAP List	Ranking (Order to do them)	Comments

GAP Chart

Goal	GAP List	Ranking (Order to do them)	Comments

GAP Chart

Goal	GAP List	Ranking (Order to do them)	Comments

GAP Chart

Goal	GAP List	Ranking (Order to do them)	Comments

Chapter 3

Get organised

1. Create a list

2. Rank the items on this list by categorising them as:

- Important

- Not Important

- Urgent

- Not Urgent

3. Optimise.

4. Plan

Get organised with CROP

Create List	Rank items on List				Optimise		Plan
	Important	Not Important	Urgent	Not Urgent	To Do List	Delegate	
Buy new uniforms	y			y			3rd Saturday of November
Write my book	y			y			
Design new course on goal setting	y			y			
Shop for groceries	y		y		2		order online for pick & drop
Write postcards to team members	y		y		1		write while in the car
Generate customer sales list	y		y			assistant	
Celebrate top customers				y			
Plan christmas event				y		assistant	
Plan slides for event on Nov 1st, Nov 8th							
Prospect new clients					3		
Book a stand at school christmas fayre							
Landscape front yard		y				assistant	

Get organised with CROP

Create List	Rank items on List				Optimise		Plan
	Important	Not Important	Urgent	Not Urgent	To Do List	Delegate	

Get organised with CROP

Create List	Rank items on List			Optimise		Plan
	Important	Not Important	Urgent	Not Urgent	To Do List	Delegate	

Get organised with CROP

Create List	Rank items on List				Optimise		Plan
	Important	Not Important	Urgent	Not Urgent	To Do List	Delegate	

Get organised with CROP

Create List	Rank items on List				Optimise			Plan
	Important	Not Important	Urgent	Not Urgent	To Do List	Delegate		

Get organised with CROP

Create List	Rank items on List				Optimise		Plan
	Important	Not Important	Urgent	Not Urgent	To Do List	Delegate	

Get organised with CROP

Create List	Rank items on List				Optimise		Plan
	Important	Not Important	Urgent	Not Urgent	To Do List	Delegate	

Get organised with CROP

Create List	Rank items on List				Optimise		Plan
	Important	Not Important	Urgent	Not Urgent	To Do List	Delegate	

Get organised with CROP

Create List	Rank items on List				Optimise		Plan
	Important	Not Important	Urgent	Not Urgent	To Do List	Delegate	

Get organised with CROP

Create List	Rank items on List				Optimise		Plan
	Important	Not Important	Urgent	Not Urgent	To Do List	Delegate	

Get organised with CROP

Create List	Rank items on List				Optimise		Plan
	Important	Not Important	Urgent	Not Urgent	To Do List	Delegate	

Connect with Doyin

Doyin Olorunfemi is a wife, mum and entrepreneur. She is passionate about helping women put their best foot forward. Her mission in life is to empower the people in her world to #LiveWell #LiveFull and #LiveOut.

Her company **MAPHer** (**Motivate Adorn Prepare Her**) runs an annual workshop every June. to inspire and train women to become better versions of themselves, and to empower them to pass it on to the next generation.

Doyin is the author of *A Letter to my Daughters*, a book written in a conversational style to encourage young women to find, develop and live their purpose; *90 Days of GRACE: Strategies for developing a Success Mindset* and *Let's Read: A Reading Log for book lovers.*

She also runs an online book club 'Minute Motivation Reading Club' on Facebook to encourage women to develop a habit of reading books that develop the mind.

On her YouTube vlogs, she teaches key life lessons in her own unique way using acronyms.

For more enquiries about her YouTube Channel, book club or workshop, or to connect with Doyin, visit:

Website - www.doyin.co.uk

Twitter - @MinMotivation

Instagram - @doyinfemi

Facebook – facebook.com/minutemotivation

Printed in Great Britain
by Amazon

80325163R00066